BIRD WATCHING

BIRD WATCHING

by *Aubrey Burns*

ILLUSTRATED BY MATTHEW KALMENOFF

FRANKLIN WATTS, INC.
575 Lexington Avenue · New York, N.Y. 10022

To Sarah Chokla Gross,
friend and believer,
this book is gratefully
dedicated

The author wishes to offer warm thanks for their help and encouragement to Mr. and Mrs. Ralph E. Ardiff, Jr., Ruth G. Kendall, Grace Lewis, Alan Paton, and William M. Pursell.

DESIGNED BY COLIN CHOW

Library of Congress Catalog Card Number: 68–11140
© Copyright 1968 by Franklin Watts, Inc.
Printed in the United States of America
1   2   3   4   5

Contents

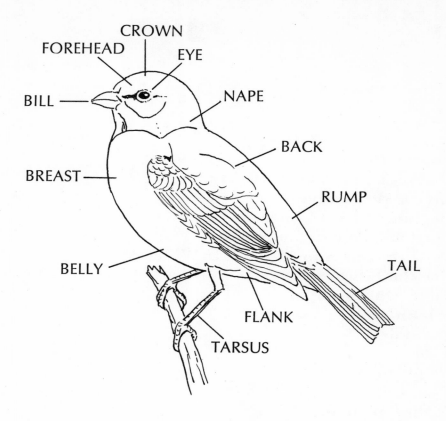

CROWN

FOREHEAD

EYE

BILL

NAPE

BACK

BREAST

RUMP

BELLY

TAIL

FLANK

TARSUS

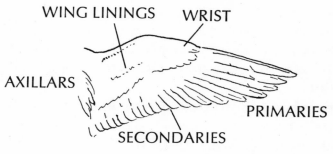

WING LININGS   WRIST

AXILLARS

PRIMARIES

SECONDARIES

UNDER SURFACE OF WING

In identification, it helps to know the parts of a bird by name.

Foreword

THERE ARE many kinds of books for bird watchers. For a beginning bird watcher there are three kinds that are especially useful:

1. Books about birds: where birds fit into the total pattern of life; how they came to be birds; how they are put together; how their parts function; how birds reproduce; their instincts, migrations, diets, and other characteristics.

2. Field guides: picture-and-description books, arranged by bird families. These guides are prepared to help bird watchers identify birds *by species* in their natural surroundings.

3. Books about bird watching. This book is one of these.

The Book List on page 58 suggests some good books about birds, some good field guides, and some other books about bird watching.

Use your library regularly. Bird watching where the birds are is your fieldwork. Backing up that fieldwork with homework, whether at home or in a library, will stimulate and explain your observations in the field and help you organize them.

A.B.

Do You Have What It Takes?

BIRD WATCHING is just what its name says: *watching birds.*

The purpose of bird watching is *getting to know birds* as they go about their daily activities.

Not everyone is the right sort of person to be a bird watcher. Some people have what it takes; others do not.

If you didn't love to play hide-and-seek when you were younger, and if you are not now interested in mystery stories, detective stories, or spy stories, you may find bird watching too exciting for you. If you don't care for adventure, exploration, and discovery, bird watching probably won't suit you. If puzzles and riddles don't tempt you, if you don't enjoy trying to outthink or outguess a shrewd opponent in a game of wits, if you are not dogged enough to hang on against odds, then bird watching is likely to bore you after a while.

Bird watching is much more than a game, but it is a game, too. It is a mystery game, a detective game, a spy game. It

IBIS   SPOONBILLS

SHARP-SHINNED HAWK
AND SPARROW

is a game of adventure and exploration and discovery. It is a game of moves and countermoves, of outguessing and out-maneuvering. It is a game that takes time and patience and close attention.

It is partly a game of chance, too. How could you possibly have known, for instance, when you happened to look out the window, that at that exact moment a sharp-shinned hawk would come swooping down into a shrub full of house sparrows to get himself a meal?

But it's not chance that keeps a bird watcher's eyes and ears alert. He knows that being on the alert for anything and everything is the only way to play this glorified hide-and-seek game with the birds.

A bird watcher must absorb many bits of information about each one of many kinds of birds. "Absorb" is the right word for it, because no one could possibly memorize all the neces-sary details. They have to soak in as the bird watcher goes along, so that gradually they become a part of him. How else, except by absorbing bird knowledge, could he know whether that low, scolding "burr" in the brush comes from a Bewick's wren, a long-billed marsh wren, or a wrentit? But, when that

3

time arrives and he finds he really does know, there will be nothing difficult about it. Knowing the little details about birds will have become second nature to him.

Live and Let Live

BIRD WATCHERS live and let live. They harm no bird, but protect all birds and other wild creatures in every way they can from the growing dangers that face them because people and civilization have crowded in upon them.

Bird watchers do this not simply out of a liking for birds, nor simply out of pity, but out of a respect for the place of birds in nature's total scheme of things. Bird watchers help not only because some birds are in some way useful or beneficial to man, but because all birds belong to the structure of life on earth.

"You are a child of the universe, no less than the trees and the stars; you have a right to be here." These words are from an inscription, dated 1692, found in Old Saint Paul's Church, in Baltimore, Maryland.

"You have a right to be here." So do the rapacious eagle and the hawk; so does the night-hunting owl; so do the carrion-eating crow and gull; so do the cowbird of America and the cuckoo of England, both of which lay their eggs in the nests of smaller birds and then go on their way; so do the flycatchers, the warblers, the swallows, the creepers, the goatsuckers, the nuthatches, the woodpeckers, and all the other insect-eaters; so do the plum-peckers, the cherry-pickers, and the other marauders that share our crops. All of these have their place. They too are children of the universe, no less than you and the trees and the stars.

Beginning Bird Watching

THE BETTER you get to know birds, the more you will want to know about them. But, for the beginning bird watcher, the first step is *to learn to identify birds.*

For several years after bird watchers first start, they need to concentrate on identifying birds—getting them sorted out and finding out which is which and what each one's name is.

First in identifying birds comes *being familiar with the appearance of birds.*

You need to see how big a bird is, what its shape is, what color—or colors—its feathers are and what patterns or markings they may have, how long its legs, neck, tail, wings, and bill are. (Some birds, for instance, may be roundish, with short bills and necks and legs, while others may be slender, with long bills and necks and legs.)

Sometimes, with only your own eyesight, learning the appearance of a bird is easy. But sometimes, even with binoculars or a telescope, it is very hard indeed.

Second in identifying birds comes *listening to birds.*

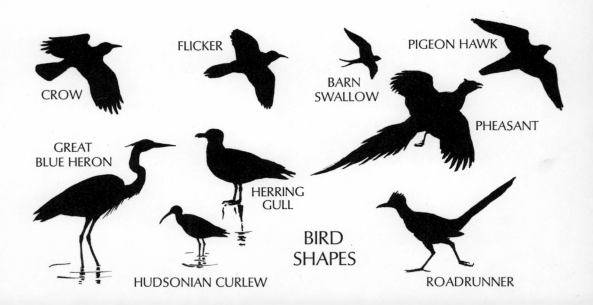

FLICKER

PIGEON HAWK

CROW

BARN SWALLOW

PHEASANT

GREAT BLUE HERON

HERRING GULL

BIRD SHAPES

HUDSONIAN CURLEW

ROADRUNNER

WHITE-BREASTED
NUTHATCH

At the same time that you are listening, watch to see *which bird said what*. When you do this, you tie together sight and sound. After you have done this often enough you will recognize a bird by its voice. From that time on, you can identify that bird without seeing it at all, if it is saying something while you are listening.

Third in identifying birds comes *observing the habits of birds*.

How a bird flies, stands, walks, swims, perches, climbs, or gets its food may be just as helpful in identifying it as its shape, color, or voice. If you see a bird going down a tree trunk headfirst, for instance, you can be sure it is a nuthatch. No other bird climbs down a tree this way.

The place where a bird is found may help you to recognize it. Some kinds of birds are always found in marshy places, some are found at the seashore, some in wooded places, and so on. Add that particular place and the bird's posture, movements, and general behavior to its appearance and its sounds, and you can identify practically any "mystery bird."

So, to begin with, observe birds to see what they look like, how they sound, and what they do and how they do it.

6

Start with What You Have

YOU ALREADY have the three most important tools for bird watching:

1. One good pair of eyes.
2. One good pair of ears.
3. One good brain behind and between them.

There are tools you can buy that are most helpful, and in due time you will have at least two of them: a field guide and binoculars. We shall have more to say about these farther on in this book.

But don't wait for binoculars, or for a field guide of your own, to start bird watching. The tools you already have are the main ones. Remember that some of the great bird watchers of years gone by never had any tools but these. And thousands of country people know their bird neighbors well, although they have no tools but their eyes, their ears, and their brains.

Learn to know just one bird at a time. One day soon you will see a bird and even before you can think, "What bird is that?" something in your head will say, "Robin." The bird pushes the button; your mind flashes the answer.

This flash is called *recognition*. How will you come to recognize robins? By getting acquainted with their colors, their ways of running and flying, the sounds they make—by watching them.

First get to know the birds around you—in your own yard, on your own schoolgrounds, in the nearest park, in nearby woods or fields, by a nearby lake or river, or at a nearby seashore or bay margin, depending on where you live.

How Do You Know Which Is Which?

"Species" is the key word in the identification of birds. "Species" is a word from the Latin, meaning "sort" or "kind." But it now belongs to almost all languages because it has become a scientific word in biology, the science of life and living things. A species is a separate sort or kind of plant or animal. (The word is spelled the same way whether we speak of one species or many species.)

A bird species is a group of birds that are almost exactly alike in certain important and basic ways. Each chooses a member of its own group for a mate, and passes this alikeness on to its young.

Whether you realize it or not, you already know some of the facts about species.

You know that it will always be baby chicks that hatch from the eggs hens lay—never ducklings or goslings. You know that all roosters crow, all hens cackle, and all baby chicks cheep.

Species guarantees the predictable "chicken-ness" of chickens, the certain "robin-ness" of robins, the dependable "crow-ness" of crows.

In hundreds of thousands of years, species sometimes do change, but this is usually a slow and gradual process.

We do not give names to each single bird, as we do to every human being. We identify birds by species.

Even though there may be many millions of birds in a species, the individual birds are so much alike that a few pictures in a bird watcher's field guide, with a paragraph or two of description, can make it possible for you to identify, *as a member of that species*, any single one of these many birds.

In some species the male is different from the female in appearance, in size, in song, in behavior, or in all of these. For

8

YOUNG SAW-WHET OWL

ADULT SAW-WHET OWL

FEMALE
WOOD DUCK

MALE
WOOD DUCK

these species, a field guide must show two pictures, or give two descriptions, to make sure that every member of that species can be identified.

In some species the young, immature bird—especially the young, immature male—does not look as it will when it is grown. In these cases there must be one more picture and description to give the help needed in identification.

In many species the male has a special coloring of feathers in the mating season. This is called *breeding plumage* or *summer plumage*. But during the rest of the year this same male has a duller and very different sort of coloring, called *winter plumage*. This winter coloring is often very much like the female's plumage. For such species, field guides must have pictures of birds in both plumages, and must have more description.

Although these many differences may be confusing, in each species all the males look alike and behave alike at the same times of year. All the females of a species look alike and behave alike at the same times of year. Each of the immature birds looks and behaves like all the other immature birds of that species.

Members of a single species do things in the same way. They like the same kinds of places to live; eat the same kinds of food; build the same kind of nests; lay eggs of about the same size, shape, and color. And if birds of a certain species habitu-

9

ally go south for the winter, all the members of the species, except for an occasional straggler who somehow missed his flight, go at about the same time and to the same kinds of places. This pattern of doing things is due to instinct, which among birds takes the place of reason.

Species that are alike in many basic ways form groups called *families*.

It is easier to be sure of a bird's family than it is to be sure of its species. You will hear people say: "I saw a goose"—or a duck, a sandpiper, an owl, a hummingbird, a swallow, a wren, a warbler. But these are not the names of species.

In North America there are 9 species of geese, nearly 40 species of ducks, 33 of sandpipers, 18 of owls, 15 of hummingbirds, 8 of swallows, 10 of wrens, and 53 of wood warblers.

Even so, it is simpler to find out which one of 53 wood warblers your "mystery bird" is, *after* you have tagged him as a warbler, than it would be to find out which one of seven or eight hundred species, in a number of different families, he belongs to.

Knowing the families is the first step toward the identification of any bird *by species*. If you know the families you can say No at once to most of the possibilities that may come to mind in identifying a bird.

Use the Library

Go to the library and find a good field guide. Its contents will be bird pictures and descriptions, *species by species*, arranged by *families*. (You will find some good field guides listed at the end of this book.)

Pick a field guide with good clear pictures in full color. Look up the family groups, one by one. Study the pictures carefully, looking for family resemblances among the species of each group.

You will see that many of the family groups have subfamilies. Ducks, swans, and geese are all subfamilies in the same larger family. There are five duck subfamilies in all, among them the mergansers. Mergansers have long, straight bills, sawtoothed at the edges. First, learn that these birds are ducks. Next, learn that they are mergansers. Finally, learn the differences between the three species of mergansers.

Here and there, among the species in the family groups you are studying, you will find a bird you already know by species. In the "Thrushes, Solitaires, and Bluebirds" group you will find your old friend the robin. Among the woodpeckers you may recognize your local flicker. Already knowing at least one member of a family will help you get acquainted with the other members of that family quickly.

After you are familiar with the families, you can begin to sort out the various species of owls, of kingfishers, of woodpeckers, and of the other bird families.

For sorting, your tool is *a knowledge of field marks*.

Field Marks

WHEN YOU are in the field—out watching birds wherever they may be—you will probably see a bird you do not recognize. You may be pretty sure what family it belongs to, and it may look a good deal like a species you know, but somehow it just isn't quite right. Something is different.

Look for that difference. Remember it—or better still, write it down. As soon as you get a chance, look the bird up. That difference is called a field mark. Field marks make it possible for ordinary bird watchers to identify birds by species in the field.

A bird's field mark may be yellow legs instead of gray or black ones. It may be a red or an orange bill. It may be a white ring around the eye. It may be a crest on top of the head. It may be a longer or a shorter tail, a differently shaped bill, or a different color or pattern on the throat, the breast, the sides, or the wings. Or it may be the way a bird twitches its wings quite often, or flips its tail up, or bobs up in front as if it had the hiccups, or teeters up and down behind, or jumps up to scratch leaves backward with both feet at the same time. It may be the way a bird holds its neck when it flies, or the way it flap-flap-flaps along steadily, or the way it flaps a little then soars for a while. It may be whether it flies high or skims just above the ground or water. (For instance, cranes always fly with their long necks stretched out, but herons and egrets fold their necks back so that their heads are just in front of their shoulders.)

There are many, many of these differences. Whatever they may be, each one of them can give you a clue to a bird species. Often these differences will settle the matter of identification on the spot. But if not, they will keep you from jumping to a wrong conclusion.

With long bird-watching experience you might figure out all these field marks by yourself. But that is the hard way, and wasteful of your time and enjoyment.

There are three shortcuts to the knowledge of field marks.

The first one, you will already know—*a good field guide.*

If you have a field guide with you as you bird-watch, you can look up your bird while it is still perched, soaring, or swimming in full view. That is very helpful, because often, besides the field mark you have noticed, there is listed another more

SOME FIELD MARKS TO LOOK FOR

TURKEY VULTURE. (Flies with wings in broad V. Tilts as it soars.)

OSPREY. (Crook in wing, black wrist mark.)

BALD EAGLE (White head and tail.)

RED-SHOULDERED HAWK. (Broad tail, broad wings, reddish shoulder patches, white bands on tail.)

GOSHAWK. (Rounded wings, long tail, gray underparts, broad white eye stripe.)

PEREGRINE FALCON. (Long, pointed wings, narrow tail, dark cap.)

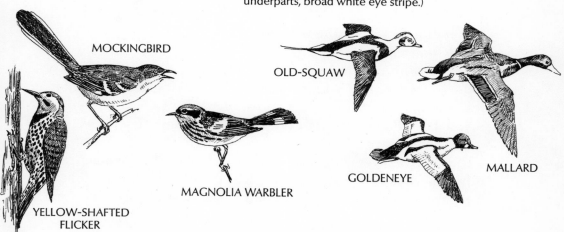

MOCKINGBIRD

OLD-SQUAW

YELLOW-SHAFTED FLICKER

MAGNOLIA WARBLER

GOLDENEYE

MALLARD

Notice breast (plain? spotted? striped?); shape of tail; wing markings.

In water birds, notice wing markings and body and head color.

important one that you had not noticed. Look at the bird again, check that point too, and pin down your identification then and there.

If you do not have a field guide with you, write down everything you have noticed about your bird. Then, as soon as you can, go to your library and look him up.

There are two excellent paperback books that cost very little but will give you a great deal of help until you can get a complete field guide: (1) *How To Know the Birds: An Introduction to Bird Recognition*, by Roger Tory Peterson; (2) *Birds: A Guide to the Most Familiar Birds*, by Herbert S. Zim and Ira N. Gabrielson. Both are excellent for beginners. Even after you have a complete field guide you will still treasure either of these books for the additional information and suggestions it contains, besides its pictures and descriptions of bird species. Either book can be bought for about a dollar or less at almost any bookstore. If the shop does not have it, the clerk can order it for you.

In the Book List at the back of this book you will find information about the complete field guides, along with information about other bird books you will want to use later.

The second shortcut to the knowledge of field marks is *looking at mounted displays of local-area birds* in cases or in natural-habitat dioramas at a museum.

This shortcut is easy for people who live in large cities where there are ornithological or natural history museums. If you live in the country or in a town or smaller city, looking at such exhibits would be possible only on a trip to a large city. If you do go on such a trip, don't forget to go to the museum. It will be well worth the trouble.

If you live where there are such exhibits, study them carefully. On your first few visits you will go away with a jumble of so many different birds in your mind that you cannot sort them

14

out. But go back again and again. Each time, some of the jumble will settle into clear impressions that you can remember.

Even more useful is a visit to the museum *after* you have been puzzled by a bird, or by several, in the field. Perhaps you couldn't pin down the difference between one gull and another, or between one sandpiper and another. Then you walk into the museum. There is your puzzler, just as you saw him alive—and there is his name tag for you, right at the front of the case. One visit to a museum *after* you have been baffled is worth several visits before it happened.

The third shortcut is the shortest cut of all: *going out with an experienced bird watcher* who (1) knows the field marks of every species you are likely to see; (2) knows, when a bird's voice is heard, what bird's voice it is; (3) knows the flight pattern (the manner of flying) of every species you are likely to

Museum natural-habitat diorama.

see, and so can name the birds that do not stop to be looked at carefully, (4) recognizes birds by their posture, body movements, and feeding habits; and (5) knows which species would be *where* this bird is *when* this bird is there.

Of course, if identifying birds is made too easy, you won't learn how to do it for yourself. The way to use the help of an expert most usefully is to sit down after your expedition, with a field guide and other books that give fuller information. Check out everything that has been told you by your expert. Do this while it is still fresh in your mind.

Then go out yourself and practice *using in the field* what you have just learned. Only in this way will you make some of that experienced bird watcher's knowledge and skill really your own. Until it becomes your own, all you will get from such help will be some free identifications that you cannot proudly claim credit for.

A bird watcher's delight is to recognize species for himself, out of his own knowledge and effort and skill. Every time you see a strange bird for the first time, and with your own eyes and mind identify it for yourself, you can add its name to your Life List with real satisfaction.

As you begin bird watching, it is of first importance to find the channels of information and advice on birds, to open them, and to keep them open.

They are:

(1) Libraries, with the help of librarians.
(2) Local Audubon societies.
(3) Experienced and knowledgeable bird watchers in your neighborhood, town, and city.
(4) The National Audubon Society.
(5) Natural history museums.

Migration

BIRDS LIVE one day at a time. Today they must find their food for today, and tomorrow they must find their food for tomorrow. Food is their fuel and they burn it up fast. They live in a hurry and are extremely active. Their hearts beat many times as fast as ours, and their body temperatures are higher. Because they use up so much energy in so short a time, they must eat a great deal and they must eat often.

That is why you may expect to find each species of bird in *the kind of place where* and at *the time of year when* the special food it needs can be found easily and plentifully.

Because of their need to find food, birds are the world's greatest travelers. Not only do they move from bough to bough, from tree to tree, from bush to bush, from field to field, and from lake to stream; they also move from mountains to valleys, from inland to the seacoast, from north to south and from south to north, from continent to continent, and even, in a few cases, almost from one pole of the globe to the other. And a few birds even move from the West to the East and back.

The larger movements are not made by one bird alone, but by groups of birds of a species traveling together. Most of these movements are from north to south and back again, and are made once a year in each direction.

"Migration" is the name for the mass journeys in the fall from nesting areas to other places (usually farther south) where

17

the birds will find their necessary food in plenty. In the spring they will return to the places from which they came.

Most migrating species follow the seasons gradually, stopping along the way in suitable places to build up their strength for the next lap of the journey. As they go south they move into late summer or early autumn, although the place they left is already in late autumn or early winter. And as they return northward they travel no faster than the northward movement of spring.

Because of migration, during the course of a year there will be four separate and distinct populations of birds in your area.

Population A: *Permanent residents.* These birds live in your area the year round. Because their food supply continues to be plentiful throughout the year they do not migrate.

Population B: *Summer residents.* These birds mate and nest in your area, and raise their families there. But because their food supply is sufficient only in spring and summer they go south in the fall to remain throughout the winter. In the spring they return to your area in time for the mating and nesting season.

Population C: *Winter visitors.* These birds are summer residents north of your area, and raise their families there. In the fall they come south to spend the winter in your area.

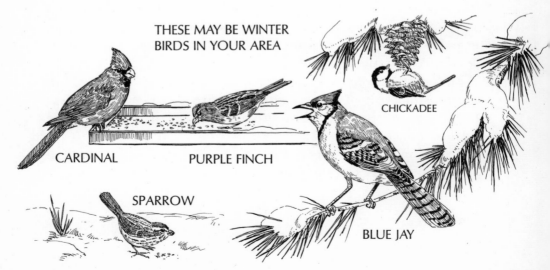

THESE MAY BE WINTER
BIRDS IN YOUR AREA

CARDINAL   PURPLE FINCH   CHICKADEE

SPARROW

BLUE JAY

YELLOW WARBLER

Population D: *Transients,* sometimes called *birds of passage.* These birds pass through your area on their way from summer homes north of you to wintering places south of you, and again on their way back to their nesting grounds in more northerly lands. They may pass through your area in a day, or in a week, or in a month. But, for however long a period they remain, this is only a stopover—to time their progress to the movement of the seasons or to rest a while or to build up their energy with food, or to do all three of these things. If a species of bird goes south by one route and returns by another, you may see its members in the spring but not in the fall—or the other way round.

Of those bird species to be seen in your area, find out as soon as you can which are permanent residents, which are summer residents, which are winter visitors, and which are transients.

The quickest way to find out is through study of a local field guide or of a local-area checklist. Ask the nearest local Audubon Society or any experienced bird watcher about checklist cards. If there is a charge for them, it probably will not be more than ten or fifteen cents. If there is no local field guide and no checklist covering your local area, you will have to dig out the information for yourself from a regular larger-area field guide, unless you can find a veteran bird watcher who is willing to go down the list in the regular field guide and tell you which birds belong to each group. Most long-time bird watchers are happy to help beginners.

Habitats

THERE ARE many different kinds of places in the world, and most of them are occupied or visited by birds; even in mid-ocean where no land is near, several bird species can be seen from ships.

Not all birds live in all places, however. Most species prefer one kind of living place because it provides the particular type of food and the general conditions they need. The needed conditions may include any of the following: cover (places to hide); open space (for instant flight or for a bird's-eye view of small birds or animals below); running water, still water, or salt water to swim in; farm animals to attract insects; freedom from enemies such as cats or hawks; warmth or coolness. The places that birds or any other animals choose to inhabit are called their *habitats*.

Some birds, such as gulls, house sparrows, starlings, crows, blackbirds, and pigeons, are quite at home in any one of several different habitats. But other birds can thrive only in one particular kind of habitat.

The following list is not complete, but it describes briefly most of the habitats preferred by various species:

1. City streets, buildings, squares, parks, old cemeteries, sidewalk trees, and backyard gardens.

2. Small towns, suburban yards and gardens, golf courses, schoolgrounds, airports, garbage dumps, and sewage-disposal plants and their outlets.

3. Farmland—plowed, planted, or harvested—orchards, and vineyards.

4. Dairy farms and livestock ranches with their feeding places, pastures, and meadows.

5. Uncultivated fields ragged with thistles, dill, teasels, tumble-

SHORE AND DUNES

SOME BIRD HABITATS

FIELDS AND MEADOWS

WOODLANDS AND BUSHY PLACES

MARSHES

weeds, wild blackberry vines, and the like.

6. Open prairie or grassy, rolling hills.

7. Deserts and semiarid wasteland.

8. Hills, canyons, or mountainsides covered with chaparral.

9. Evergreen forests.

10. Deciduous forests—trees that drop their leaves in autumn.

11. High mountains with snow-watered ravines and mountain meadows.

12. Rock cliffs or outcroppings.

13. Freshwater marshes with cattails and other water growths.

14. Freshwater creeks and ponds surrounded by willow thickets or other brushy cover.

15. Rivers and the islands in them, and riverbanks.

16. Swamps.

17. Lakes and dammed reservoirs.

18. Saltwater bays, inlets, estuaries, and lagoons having tidal waters and mudflats.

19. Saltwater marshes.

20. Beaches and windswept dune areas.

21. Coastal rocks, including "chimneys" and other rocks standing alone, apart from the shore cliffs.

22. The open ocean offshore, beyond sight of land.

Birds are partial to *edges*. It is true that some birds are found in mid-ocean, in the depths of a forest, in the middle of a large pasture, in the middle of a bay or lake, or in the middle of a large lawn. But many more birds are found at the edge of town, or along the fence between fields and a highway right-of-way, or at the edge of a forest (which may also be the edge of an uncultivated field or of a grassy meadow with scattered oak trees). Multitudes of birds are found at the edge of the sea and the edges of bays, lakes, and rivers, which are also the edges of whatever sort of land lies next to the water.

Tides

SHOREBIRDS ORDER their lives by the tides. (In coastal areas the newspapers regularly publish tide tables, covering about a week at a time. These tables list the times, day by day, when the tide will be high and when it will be low, and also indicate how high and how low the tides will be.)

Shorebirds feed chiefly on the seafood uncovered by the tide as it goes out. Some take food from the transparent shallow water itself. In falling back, the water leaves tiny swimmers exposed to sharp eyes and sharper beaks.

Hosts of hungry shorebirds follow the water's edge as it withdraws. On almost-level tideflats the birds move gradually farther and farther from dry land—sometimes as much as half a mile or more. Later, as the tide returns, the shorebirds backtrack before it, coming closer and closer to the high-tide mark.

Some shorebirds get up early or stay up late if the tide starts going out in the shadowy dawn or is still out while dusk is gathering. But in general, shorebirds hunt by daylight and sleep at night. For watching them, choose a daytime low tide.

"Puddle ducks," which feed by dabbling, plowing the mud, or tipping up their tails in the shallow water, move outward

YELLOWLEGS

and then back again with the tide as the shorebirds do. The two groups go and come together—the ducks on the water side of the lapping edge, facing the shore; the shorebirds on the mud side, facing the sea.

But diving ducks keep to the deeper water. Look for them when the tide comes in, for then they will be at their closest point to shore. At low tide they are likely to be too far out for good watching. The same thing is true of sea ducks.

At high tide the multitudes of shorebirds disappear. Where do they go? Often to a levee of clods about the same size and color as themselves, close to a quiet backwater or lagoon. Even more often they seek out the bank of a winding channel in the midst of a wide saltwater marsh, just far enough from any access point to discourage most bird watchers, and just low enough behind marsh growths to escape the searching lenses of binoculars focused from the nearest solid ground. Wherever they gather, the shorebirds huddle so tightly together that they are difficult to see because they look more like a patch of plants or earth than like individual living creatures.

Night herons feed most often at night. At bedtime, if you live near tideflats, you may hear the loud "Quock!" of a night heron breaking the silence. Or, if you wake up in that darkest hour before daybreak, you may hear it again. If you should be near tideflats in time to see the first hint of the coming dawn, you may see, dark against the faint grayness of the sky, large birds with steadily beating wings. They will come slowly from the direction of the shore, by ones and twos and threes, with intervals between. One of them may cry out "Quock!" These are night herons going home to their wooded roosting place to sleep all day. Yet from time to time you may see a night heron on a tideflat or in a saltwater marsh during the day, if the tide is low.

Land Birds

Owls ARE also night hunters, and so are the so-called goatsuckers: whip-poor-wills, nighthawks, and their kindred.

The goatsuckers are well camouflaged against daytime viewing, but may be seen readily enough in the dusk as they catch flying insects while they themselves are in full flight.

Owls, too, may be seen at dusk, moving softly and silently like thick black moths in the gloom of early darkness. By day, if you find pellets of fur and bones on the ground underneath trees and if you stare persistently enough up through the branches, you may glimpse roosting owls. The pellets are the rejected parts of the owls' prey, disgorged from their crops.

Mockingbirds may be heard singing at almost any hour of the night, but especially from the first faint paling of the morning sky until after the sun has risen.

Killdeer are often heard crying long after dark. Hummingbirds, because they are almost constantly on the move and use up more energy than other birds, stay up later to feed and are out earlier.

But all day-birds, however early they may roost and however late they may start their day, need extra fuel to warm them through the night. And they are ravenous for food in the morning. So the best times to go land-bird watching are the first hour of daylight and the last.

Many birds laze through the hottest hours of summer days, as people in the tropics take siestas. But most birds do feed from time to time during the daylight hours, especially in winter. A few feed slowly all day long, hardly ever stopping. But some are able to get enough to eat in a short time.

SLATE-COLORED JUNCOS

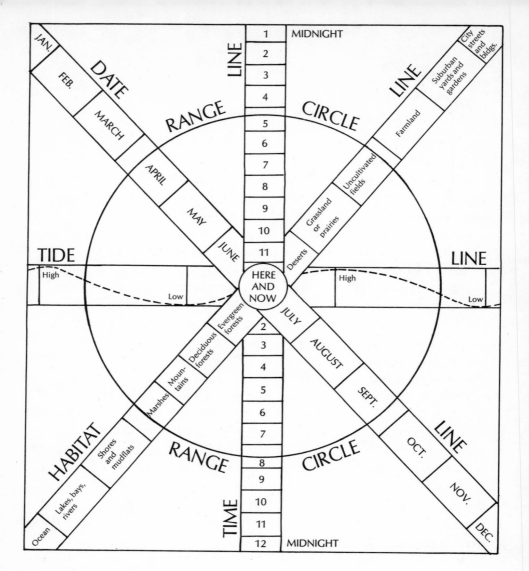

The "Here and Now" Chart

THIS CHART has been prepared to help you focus your own knowledge and the information in your field guide on one particular place and one particular time.

26

The authors of field guides describe all the birds that are likely to be seen in any part of a large geographical area at any time of year or at any time of day. But you live in one particular place. What is important to you is this: What birds can be seen *here*?

When you go out to watch birds, it is on one particular date and at one particular hour. What is important to you is this: What birds can be seen here *now*?

On the chart, the small circle in the middle is your *Here and Now* point. It represents *where you are, and when*. But it also must represent *where the bird is, and when*, before the two of you can meet. Either he must come where you are, or you must go where he is.

You can use this chart as a reminder to guide you through the steps that will help you answer questions like these:

1. Which species may I expect to find where I am going, at the time when I will be there?

2. Where should I go, and when, in order to find a bird of a certain species?

3. Is it possible that the species I think this bird is could have been where I saw the bird, at the time I saw it? If not, what other similar species might possibly have been there at that time?

Imagine that the *Range Circle* and the central *Here and Now* spot are fixed, but that the four crosslines (*Date, Habitat, Tide,* and *Time*) are in grooves, and can be pushed or pulled, either forward or backward. Imagine yourself setting them one by one for any bird-finding calculation you may wish to make.

Now suppose it is March and you are in a coastal area. You want to find a black-crowned night heron.

First, check your field guide to find out if this heron's range includes all of the area where you are. If so, the heron is within

27

the *Range Circle*. (If a species is not included in any of the four populations of your area—permanent residents, summer residents, winter visitors, or transients—you are not in the range of that species, and need look no further.)

Second, check your field guide to find out if the black-crowned heron is a resident of your area in March. If it is, imagine the *Date Line* sliding down so as to place March directly under the *Here and Now* point.

Third, check your field guide to find out this heron's habitats. They are "freshwater swamps, lake margins, bay shores, and tidal marshes." Do you have one of these nearby? If so, imagine the *Habitat Line* sliding along until the correct habitat rests directly under the *Here and Now* point.

Fourth, check the tide tables in your local newspapers, make the necessary readjustments for your target habitat, and find out at what time the tide there will be going out during the dusk-to-daylight hours. Then imagine the *Tide Line* sliding along until a point about one-third of the way, going from "High" to "Low," is directly under the *Here and Now* point.

Fifth, imagine the *Time Line* sliding until the time directly under the *Here and Now* point is the same as that when the tide will be going out (and about one-third of the way from "High" to "Low") during the dusk-to-daylight hours, preferably at or near dusk or daylight.

Now your *Here and Now Chart* is all set. The proper date, habitat, tide, and time all meet within the *Range Circle* at the *Here and Now* point. Go to the indicated habitat, on the indicated date, at the indicated time, and you will have the combination of circumstances that make for the greatest likelihood of your finding a black-crowned night heron.

A Bird-Watching Ramble

A COUNTRY DOG goes out for a run on the roads or through the fields with his nose twitching, his ears lifted, his eyes open. Every movement of the breeze brings him odors that are his bulletins. They tell him, "A rabbit has been here lately. There is a skunk a long way off, over in that direction. Not very long ago, a cow was about where I am now." All his senses are alert. Each sense tells another what there is to be found, and where.

So you can explore your world when you go for a bird-watching ramble all by yourself. Your nose will not help you much. But your ears, with their sound-gathering outer receivers, are sensitive direction-finders and distance-measurers.

First, focus them. Turn them this way and that, including upward, with your hands cupped around them.

At the same time, tune them. Tune *out* the sounds of traffic, of the wind, of trains, of boat whistles, of foghorns, of the falling rain, of jet planes, of the breaking surf, of the ball game on somebody's transistor radio. Tune out even the songs and cries of louder birds such as jays, gulls, or crows. Tune *in* the smaller sounds you want—the click and squeak of a hummingbird; the buzzy, breathy whisper of some warblers; the tiny, thin voices of bushtits, the twitter of swallows, the peeps of sandpipers. You can do this by concentrating on the lesser noises.

In a few moments your ears will get a fix on a bird's location, if the bird is saying something and keeps on saying it.

You can tune in your eyes, too. They can blank out background or foreground or side areas and focus through, over, under, or between—upon one tiny speck far beyond. That speck may be a 4½-inch, yellowish-green bird on a twig almost concealed by greenish-yellow leaves, as much as 50 or 100 feet away. Change

29

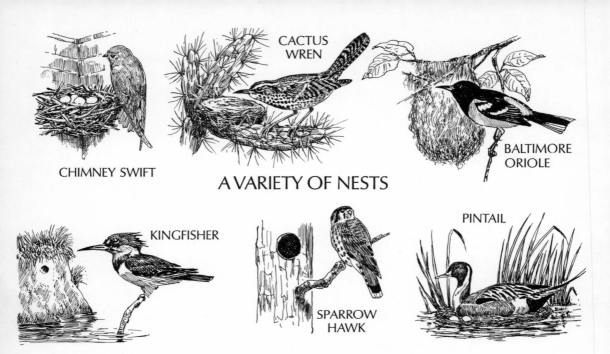

CHIMNEY SWIFT

CACTUS WREN

BALTIMORE ORIOLE

A VARIETY OF NESTS

KINGFISHER

SPARROW HAWK

PINTAIL

your focus for one second and you have lost him.

So, tune in your eyes. Let your ears direct them. If a straight look shows nothing, try your peripheral vision (from the corner of your eye), which is especially good at noticing movement. Let your eyes rove about the target area until you catch something moving. It may be your bird.

But if he sees you looking at him he may fly up, or fly down, or disappear behind leaves or branches. If he does, don't jump up and follow him. Remember that he has wings and you do not. It is much more likely that another bird, or several, will come where you are than that you would be able to track down the bird that has flown. Do not be in a hurry.

Be still and wait. Birds see and hear people coming. Some birds are bold, but most are shy. At the noise and movement of your approach they withdraw and are still.

But if you have come quietly, as you always should, and if now you remain still, after a little time the birds will relax.

Gradually, at first, and then more freely, they will resume the activities you interrupted.

Never move suddenly or loudly. A bird can get used to a quiet watcher. Once accustomed to your presence, many birds will go about their business without fear, even if you do make small, slow, gradual movements.

If you must move, stop between movements, as the black-bellied plover does when *he* is watching *you*. (He seems to take one or two steps, then freeze in the very middle of the next step, not even putting his raised foot all the way down, and wait as he watches.)

And remember that birds seem to notice motion forward, toward them, less than motion toward one side or the other.

Some species are "cover-lovers." They stay out of sight most of the time. When they are fairly sure there is no unfamiliar or dangerous creature about, they venture out. But they stay close to the cover, and at the first unexpected sound or movement they disappear again. If you move toward their hiding place, they scurry from cover to cover and are gone.

At mating time, birds sing more than at other times, and so are easier to locate. Many species make quite different sounds at other times of year—sounds that are lower pitched, not so loud, and shorter. And some simply make no sound at all in winter.

So, in the winter, it is mainly up to your eyes. And in the winter, day comes late and night comes early, and weekdays are full of other activities. Most people have to do most of their winter bird watching on weekends.

But be bird watching all the time. Not that you should stop whatever you are doing every time you see a bird; but as you go about your business or outdoor fun, do let your eyes and ears and the half-conscious part of your mind be aware of birds.

31

Be Alert for New Species

WHENEVER YOU see a bird you cannot identify, notice its field marks. Look for its similarities to birds you already know. This will help you spotlight the differences.

You may see some small brownish birds feeding on the ground beside the road, near some dry weeds. You cannot place them exactly, and you do not have a field guide with you. So you get as good a look at them as you can before they slip under cover, and you go away with this sort of thought working in your mind:

"They're about the color and shape of vesper sparrows, with the streaked sides and white outside tail feathers. About the size of vesper sparrows, too. But they had *thinner, sharper* bills than sparrows have. And now I remember that I saw two or three of them sort of *wagging their tails*—not back and forth, but up and down." (These birds, when you look them up, will turn out to have been pipits. And if you can remember that their legs were dark instead of light, you can be sure they were water pipits, not Sprague's pipits.)

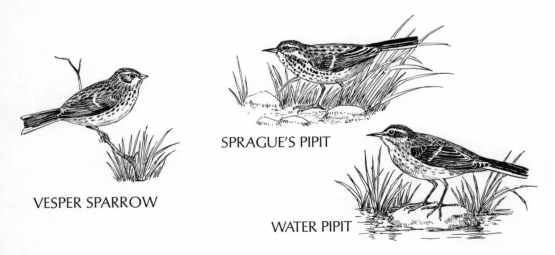

SPRAGUE'S PIPIT

VESPER SPARROW

WATER PIPIT

SONG SPARROW

Watch All Birds Always

DON'T JUST watch for new birds. Discovering a species new to you and adding it to your Life List is certainly more exciting than watching the robins, crows, grackles, jays, starlings, or doves that you already know. But there is always more to learn about these familiar birds: their different plumages, how they look from different angles of view, how they behave at different times and under different circumstances—especially in the mating and nesting seasons. Learn the pattern of their flight, their posture as they walk, the way they get their food, how they build their nests, and how they brood their eggs. Each species has its own particular way of doing things.

Nearly all species make more than one sound. They have alarm calls, scold tones, chirps or twitters at dusk and dawn. Some species have more than one real song. Even those that have only one song often vary it, adding a note or two sometimes, leaving off part at another time.

And just as there are good and poor voices among people, so individual birds within a species vary a great deal in their vocal equipment and vocal skill. It is important that you be able to recognize a variety of individual performers as song sparrows, for instance. Otherwise you will worry yourself needlessly trying to find out what new species one of them might be—when actually he isn't. The voices of song sparrows vary more than those of most other bird species.

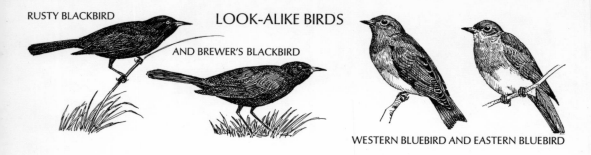

RUSTY BLACKBIRD

LOOK-ALIKE BIRDS

AND BREWER'S BLACKBIRD

WESTERN BLUEBIRD AND EASTERN BLUEBIRD

Don't Take Any Birds for Granted

FOR DAYS a bird watcher drove past a tall tree on his way to work. He saw small birds among the half-leafless top branches, caught a hint of color, said to himself, "House finches," and went on his way. But one morning there was one larger bird there, so he stopped to see what it was. When he actually *looked*, he saw a robin—but he also saw that those "house finches" were really cedar waxwings.

One bird watcher looked at a tideflat and saw a line of long-legged, black-and-white birds wading in the shallow ripples and sweeping their upcurved long bills through the water like sickles. "Avocets," he said, and went on his way. But another bird watcher, not in such a hurry, watched those same avocets, noticed that one of them had longer legs (red, at that!), was black on the top of its head, on the back of its neck, and on its back and wings, and had a straight, and shorter, bill. And because he had taken nothing for granted, he was able to add to his Life List a black-necked stilt.

In the long run, it will pay you to be suspicious of the common and the expected. For among the birds that you don't really watch (because they are "just pigeons," "just gulls," "just sparrows," just the plain old everyday nobodies) is the best place for a lonely stranger, away from his own group's range, to conceal himself—especially if he looks a good deal like his present, and to you familiar, companions.

34

ROBIN AND VARIED THRUSH

Knowing the Known Leads to the Unknown

THE COMMON everyday birds have relatives—other species of the same bird family—which are very like their more familiar cousins. When you do come across one of these relatives, unless you really know the birds you think you know, right down to the fine points, you are likely to dismiss the stranger as just one more of a species you no longer notice carefully.

For instance, the varied thrush is very much like the robin in size and in behavior. It is commonly called the Oregon robin. The Brewer's blackbird is quite similar to the rusty blackbird—and also to the brown-headed cowbird. Even the starling can be taken for a blackbird, although it belongs to a quite different family. There are several jays, all about the same size, and most of them are partly or entirely blue. At first glance many sparrows look alike. The same is true of many warblers.

Of course, most of these look-alikes can be told apart by ear, if they sing or call while you are watching—and if you can be sure which song belongs to the bird you already know. So learn the songs and sounds of all the species that are plentiful around you. Once you know all of them well, you will recognize the presence of a new voice the moment it joins the customary voices, and you can start looking for the newcomer while he is still singing. And once you have seen the bird with his beak open while you hear that song coming from him, you have him and his song in mind for keeps.

35

Always bird-watch. Be alert for new species, but watch all birds always. And don't take any birds for granted, because really knowing the known leads to the unknown.

It's Not Easy

BIRD WATCHING is not easy. Strangely enough, that is the very reason why it is fascinating to so many people. If it were easy, an intelligent person would not find it challenging for very long. But because it is difficult, he usually finds himself becoming more and more interested in it.

The first difficulties in bird watching have been built in by nature over the ages—built into the birds' colors and patterns of plumage, built into the colors and patterns of their eggs, and built into their instincts. *Camouflage* and *concealment* have helped birds as we know them to survive through countless ages. Many birds and their eggs, and often their nests and young, are hard to see.

Some birds at rest look like dead leaves. Others look like an old twig stub covered with lichens. In evergreen trees where small cones grow directly from large branches, a bird sitting on a limb appears to be just one more cone. You may see him fly into the tree, but then he simply disappears. The bittern, streaked brown on breast and throat, stands among rushes with his long bill pointing straight up—and just doesn't seem to be there. So birds hide in plain sight.

Other birds have the knack of always being just on the other side of a leaf from you—or of a branch, or of a tree trunk—and of staying there while you wait and gaze and wait. If they do move, they do so suddenly, and quickly stop moving on the far side

KILLDEER NEST
(Spotted eggs blend
into background.)

BARRED OWL
(Streaked plumage
hard to see in trees.)

WHIP-POOR-WILL
(Dark, speckled plumage
hard to see against
background.)

BIRD CAMOUFLAGE

BITTERN
(Freezes into position with
head pointed upward like
marsh plants.)

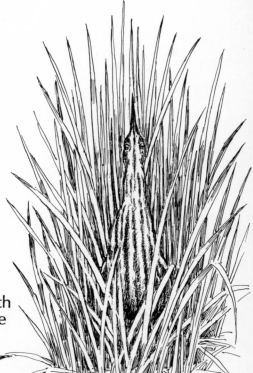

of another leaf, branch, or trunk. Birds also seem to know just how far they need to go into a bush or a thick growth of vines or wild grasses in order to be out of sight.

Just as you start to look at it, a loon or a grebe will disappear by diving or simply sinking out of sight. You keep watching the spot where the bird went down, waiting for him to come up. And you wait. Finally you discover that he has come up far from there, and is now just going down again.

Birds that don't hide may fly so fast and zigzag so often that your eye simply cannot follow rapidly enough to pick out their markings. In your early days of looking at swallows, you are watching for a square, notched, or forked tail. You are looking for a dusky throat, a dark band between throat and breast, a band across the forehead. You are looking for black, blue, green, or brown on the back and wing tops. But as a swallow approaches, suddenly he has swerved off; now he reverses his field; up he goes, then around and down.

Well, face it—you've lost him. The swallow you are now trying to follow is actually another swallow altogether.

Camouflage, concealment, tricky maneuvering, and blinding speed—these are not the only things that make bird watching difficult.

In the early morning, birds between you and the dawn light appear to be black silhouettes, so that all you have to go by is shape and size and movement. In the very late afternoon the sun may so blind you that westward birds can only be guessed at. In the dusk you will see silhouettes again, as you did in the dawn.

During the day there is the constant problem, on sunny days, of keeping the sun at your back. Even this does not solve the problem of the midday sun in summer.

Finally, you will usually be on foot, while birds can fly. The

tangle of brambles, the treacherous water and mud hidden under
a wide expanse of marsh weeds and grasses, open channels of water,
thickets of matted and sometimes thorny shrubs and small trees,
or forbidding fences posted NO TRESPASSING—any one of these
can stop *you*, but never the birds. And even if you manage to
get a fix on a puzzling bird or a mixed raft of ducks through binoculars or even a telescope, nothing prevents the birds from flying
off to the next county or diving or gliding serenely out of sight
behind a great clump of rushes.

These are some of the difficulties a bird watcher must expect.
But he need not expect to meet all of them at once. Each will
present itself in its season; and overcoming it will bring him
much of the excitement and satisfaction of the chase.

Keeping Your Bird-Watching Records

SOME BIRD watchers keep daily lists of birds seen and identified (with the number of individuals seen at each one of several locations); they keep trip lists, weekly lists, monthly lists, yearly lists, and of course, their Life List.

There are other bird watchers who keep only their Life List.

Every bird watcher should keep a Life List. This is his master record.

Your Life List should record:

1. *Each species positively identified by you,* from your beginning bird-watching days all through your life.

2. The *date* of your *first* identification of each species.

3. The *place* of that first identification.

Your Life List should reflect your personal integrity. No species should ever be entered on that list unless you yourself have certainly and beyond doubt identified that species at a particular time and place, and are prepared to defend your identification against any question raised by any person at any time.

But even more important, you should be prepared to defend that identification against your own doubts. If a doubt persists, you should be ready to strike that species off your Life List until you can restore it later in absolute certainty.

There is one other list you can keep that will help you greatly: your "mystery bird" list.

A "mystery bird" is one you have seen or heard, or both, but have not yet been able to identify for sure. A list of such birds is a waiting place for prospects not yet eligible to be admitted to your Life List.

If your "mystery bird" was one seen too briefly to permit a full check of all his field marks, write down what you did see. Write down also what you heard (in words or musical notation, or by diagram), or try to describe it. Later you may see him again and add to your notes on him the length of his tail, the bars on his wings, the color of his throat or breast. Meanwhile you are checking the field guides, looking for a picture and description that will fit him. Many likely prospects have had to be rejected because they never come near your area, or they have some additional marking you are sure your bird did not have.

One day, perhaps, you will be listening to birdsong records and something will nudge your memory. Where have you heard a call like that? It sounds like your "mystery bird." Check back on the record to make sure which bird sang that, then go to your field guide. It may be that the bird's song is translated there as "Lord Peterkin" instead of the "Our feet are thin" you had written down. But you may have your "mystery bird" in a corner.

Now, do the picture and description in the field guide fit him? Is the place where you saw or heard him within the range given in the field guide? Do the time when, and the place where, you saw him match up with his settings on the *Date Line*, the *Habitat Line,* and the *Time* or *Tide Line* so that the lines cross each other properly at the *Here and Now* point of the *Here and Now Chart?* If so, he *is* your bird and can be transferred to your Life List.

Aside from your Life List and your "mystery bird" list, keep just those records that will give you the information you need. If you feel a need for an additional record, set it up. If you feel that you are becoming a slave to a record system you do not really need, drop it. Bird watching should bring not drudgery or boredom, but joy and satisfaction.

41

How To Attract Birds

THERE ARE two ways to get close to birds so that you can watch them.

The first and best way is to go where the birds are.

The other way is to get the birds to come where you are.

Even if you go where the birds are as often as you can, it is good to be able to watch birds on the days when you are at home.

Most of the birds you can attract to your house will be common ones. But this daily gathering of familiar birds will in turn occasionally attract uncommon and unfamiliar ones that happen to be passing by. Some of these may be rare in your area— possibly rare even in your state or province—and would be prizes for your Life List.

How do you go about attracting birds?

The first thing you will probably think of is food.

Different species of birds eat different foods. Some are happy to get the packaged wild bird mix of small weed, grass, and grain seeds. Some that will eat those seeds, and others that will not, will be delighted with sunflower seeds. Still others prefer whole or cracked corn kernels, or peanuts or bread crumbs. A few species will eat just about anything you put out. Find out what foods the various birds like, and put out what the birds in your area at the time will eat.

Many species will not fly up to a hanging feeder or high tray. They are ground feeders, and for them food should be scattered on the ground. If possible, scatter the food on a bit of slightly rough bare earth, partly covered with fallen leaves. Each bird species is most comfortable eating what it is used to, in its accustomed way.

Woodpeckers seldom eat at a feeder, but they will peck at a suet holder on a tree trunk.

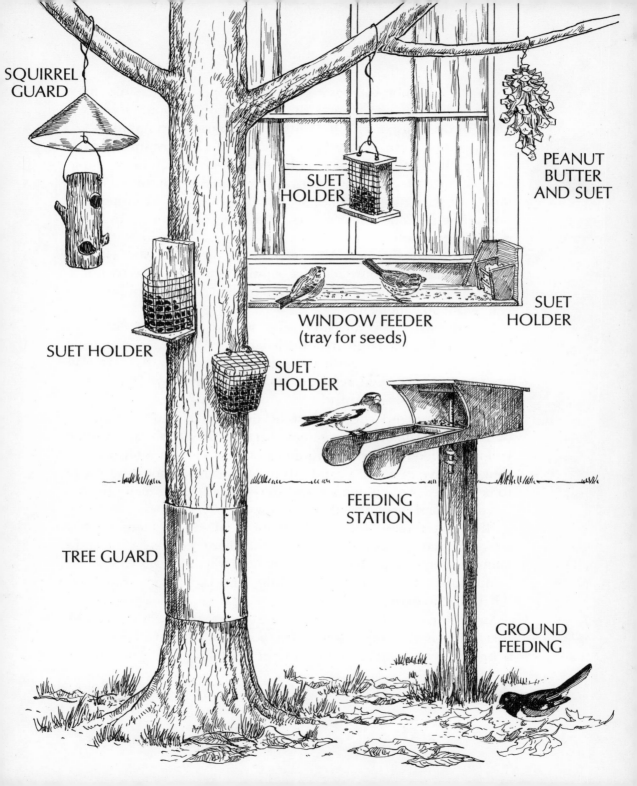

SQUIRREL
GUARD

PEANUT
BUTTER
AND SUET

SUET
HOLDER

SUET
HOLDER

WINDOW FEEDER
(tray for seeds)

SUET HOLDER

SUET
HOLDER

FEEDING
STATION

TREE GUARD

GROUND
FEEDING

Hawks will not eat your grain, but some of them do have an appetite for one item that is plentiful at your feeders—small birds. They may also drink from your water supply.

You should think twice before you open up a feeding station, whether it is a single tray with small seeds on it or a whole smorgasbord of different offerings for different tastes. To the birds, the fact that you have set up this free-lunch counter is a promise that you will keep it going. In the winter this can mean life or death to them.

Bird food costs money. And keeping the trays filled and cleaned is a daily chore. If your feeder is popular, you may have 65 house sparrows or 24 mourning doves or 50 redwings busily gobbling up your grain on a single day.

It can easily cost you fifty cents a day, or fifteen dollars a month, to keep a large free-lunch counter going. Do you have fifteen dollars every month to spend on hungry birds? Are you prepared to clean and refill and rake up every day? If not, better not start!

The cleaning-up chores must be done often and thoroughly, because where many birds gather together the droppings of some will fall on food that will be eaten by others. And since birds sometimes do have diseases, a carelessly kept feeding station may prove to be a breeder of epidemics, and so cost the lives of many birds.

Your second thought will be about water.

Birds get thirsty, even when there is plenty of food. If they are not near a lake or stream, and there has been no rain lately, thirst is a problem you can help them solve.

But drinking is not the only thing that birds want water for. They need to bathe.

Since birds will drink the same water they bathe in, the best thing is running water. Next best is a drip arrangement—a bucket with a hole or two in the bottom hung from a tree

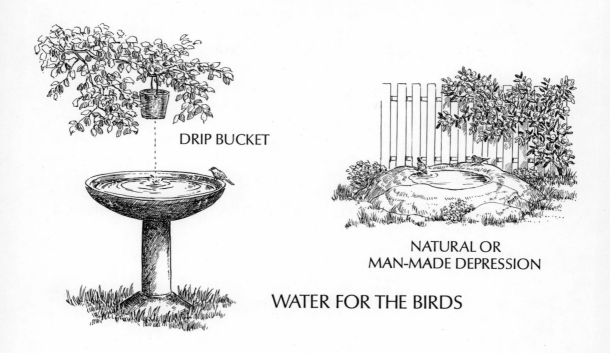

DRIP BUCKET

NATURAL OR
MAN-MADE DEPRESSION

WATER FOR THE BIRDS

limb, to keep the water changing drop by drop. The basin below the drip should be shallow, deepening gradually toward the middle. If it is deep, it should have rocks in it so that small birds can have footing without going completely underwater.

If the water cannot be running or dripping, then change it every day or two, washing out the container each time.

Birds that scratch up grubs or other insects from under decaying leaves will not want to eat your grain. Birds that pick insects from tree bark or catch them in the air may never join the group at your feeder. But these birds may be glad to drink and bathe in the water you provide.

There is another kind of birdbath that is easy to provide in dry weather. Scoop out a small area. Sift some clean, dry dirt until it is powdery. Fill the area with it, making it just an inch or so deep. Birds will take dust baths there, to get rid of body parasites that trouble them beneath their feathers. From time to time, change the old dust powder for new.

Your third thought will be for safety.

While they are eating or drinking or bathing, birds need to be free from danger and from interruption by sudden noises or sudden movements. Birds are watchful—quick to take fright and fly away.

To birds, safety means enough *open space* to give them a

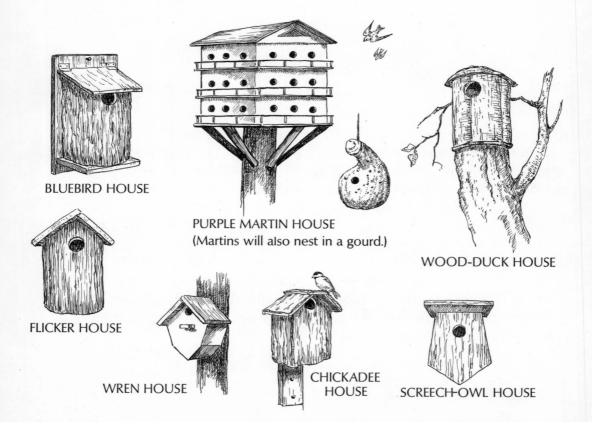

BLUEBIRD HOUSE

PURPLE MARTIN HOUSE
(Martins will also nest in a gourd.)

WOOD-DUCK HOUSE

FLICKER HOUSE

WREN HOUSE

CHICKADEE HOUSE

SCREECH-OWL HOUSE

good view of any hawks, cats, dogs, or people who may be approaching. And it means *places of refuge*—places they can escape to quickly in order to get out of reach or out of sight. See that such places are handy.

Next you will think of nesting places.

Winter visitors will not use nesting places. Neither will birds of passage. But some summer residents will use them, and so will some permanent residents.

Begin by making sure which species do breed in your area, and of those, which ones are known to accept birdhouses for nesting. Then provide houses for those species only, and provide for each species exactly the kind of dwelling it will feel at home in. You need not try to house everybody. You can choose one favorite species you would like to have nesting near you, put up its favorite kind of house, and let all other species nest wherever they please. (There is no guarantee that a nesting pair will actually move in. If they do, that will be a tribute to your offering.)

If you want to go into bird attracting in a very small way, just put out bread crumbs, sunflower seeds, and the wild bird mix of seeds on a tray by a window, and provide a shallow pan of water. In the winter, in cold climates, add suet to the menu. Keep this small setup cleaned and filled, and you can attract quite a few birds without making too big or too expensive an operation of it.

If you do set up even as modest a feeding station as this, do not neglect to arrange for protection from cats.

If you are particularly interested in feeding birds, two books can be highly recommended to you. They are *The Bird Watcher's Guide*, by Henry Hill Collins, Jr. (pages 65–90)—this may be out of print, but your library may have it—and *Bird Watchers and Bird Feeders*, by Glenn O. Blough.

47

DOGWOOD
(Scarlet tanager.)

TRUMPET VINE
(Hummingbird.)

RED CEDAR
(Cedar waxwing.)

CRAB APPLE
(Tufted titmouse.)

BAYBERRY
(Catbird.)

CORNELIAN CHERRY
(Evening grosbeak.)

PLANT SHRUBS TO ATTRACT BIRDS

What Bird Watching Can Lead To

BIRD WATCHING is its own excuse for being. It is a satisfaction in itself. But branching off from bird watching there are roads that, if you follow them, can lead to further satisfactions.

If you use a camera as an aid to bird identification in the field, or to illustrate your bird-watching notes and sighting records, you may become deeply interested in bird photography. Color film, flashlight equipment, telescopic lenses, or a motion-picture camera may lead you on to a professional career.

There is also a fascinating hobby or career to be made in recording bird songs (and other bird sounds) in the field. This in turn could lead to the scientific study of these songs and sounds. Study from a technical, tonal-vibration point of view is one direction this might take. In another direction, study of the meaning of these songs and sounds as communication would be a valuable contribution.

The migrations of birds arouse the curiosity of many bird watchers. Learning what is known already about this subject increases that interest. Next comes helping to add to that knowledge. At stations operated under scientific supervision, birds are carefully caught and banded, then released. Later, reports are

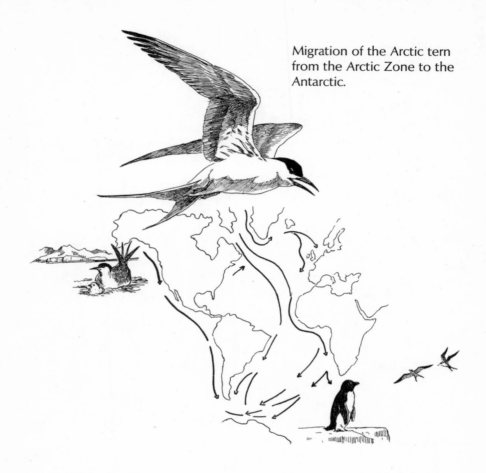

Migration of the Arctic tern from the Arctic Zone to the Antarctic.

received from other stations, and from other bird watchers. Reports also are made *to* other banding stations when trapped birds are wearing bands *from* these stations. This interchange increases knowledge of the ranges of species and of their migration routes and travel schedules. These stations can sometimes use volunteer helpers in this work. Some bird watchers graduate into staff employment in this program.

50

Others take up the intensive study of the life history of a single species. They define all its known characteristics and try to discover others. They examine its mating and nesting habits, its way of caring for its young, how large its nesting territories are, and how they are claimed and defended. They study its habitat, its diet, its range. If it migrates, the dates of its departures and arrivals —both at its destinations and at way points—are carefully scheduled. Much of this information may already be common knowledge, but there is always more to be found out.

Some people may prefer to learn how a variety of different species deal with one particular part of their existence. For example, there is the family life of birds. That is a broad subject—too broad to be covered entirely in very much depth. But it can be taken in smaller sections: courting displays, or rivalry conflicts at mating time, or the nests birds build, or the care and feeding of nestlings, or teaching the fledglings to fly.

Some bird watchers keep complete and continuous records of the comings and goings of all species at one particular place (for instance, their own homes). They keep track of the arrival time of summer and winter visitors; the times of arrival and departure of migrants passing through; the number of individual birds of each species observed there; which species mated and nested

Metal tag

How to handle a bird when banding.

there; and all other information they can obtain that can contribute to larger studies of birdlife over wide areas such as a single state, the United States, or North America. Such information will be much appreciated by any of the experts in the field of bird finding.

The study of bird populations and their distribution in small areas, in large areas, or in the world challenges many people who are interested in birds. Is each species becoming more numerous or is it shrinking in numbers? Is it becoming more widespread or more restricted in range? And when these questions are answered, the next question is, Why? (And for declining species, What can be done about it?) Of course, this is too much for any one person to tackle alone. But as in the cases of bird finding and birdbanding, your help can be valuable when it is added to the help of other bird watchers.

Some young bird watchers will go on to become full-fledged ornithologists, perhaps associated with the department of ornithology at some university, or with an ornithological museum, or with some other bird-centered agency.

Other bird watchers may become professional naturalists at bird sanctuaries or wildlife refuges.

Some will write books or magazine articles about birds.

And those with the talent for it may devote their lives to drawing or painting birds for the illustration of bird books and for many other uses.

Most of us, of course, will follow one of the many occupations of ordinary people everywhere—careers not related to ornithology or to bird watching. But as on-the-side, part-time bird watchers, we will have the magic of wings about us always.

Aids to Bird Watching

1. A public or school library well stocked with books.
2. Field guides. To avoid spending any money at all, borrow from the library any one, or all, of the guides described in the Book List that follows this section. If you can spend only a little money, buy first the paperback book *How To Know the Birds*, by Roger Tory Peterson, or *Birds*, by Herbert S. Zim and Ira N. Gabrielson. (*See* page 14 and Book List.)

   If there is a local-area field guide (such as *Enjoying Birds in Upper New York State*) published for your area, it may be inexpensive and will serve you well as long as you do not plan to watch birds outside your vicinity. It might well be your second purchase. Many such guides are listed in the section

"Regional Publications," under "Suggested Reference Material" in the eastern and western volumes of *A Guide to Bird Finding*, by Olin Sewall Pettingill, Jr. (*see* Book List). The Audubon Society also lists a number of such books in its catalog of publications.

When you are ready for a field guide of larger scope, the least expensive guide, and the only one that covers all of North America north of Mexico in one volume, is the paperback edition of *Birds of North America*, by Robbins, Bruun, and Zim (*see* Book List). It costs about three dollars. It is an excellent and convenient guide.

For about five dollars you can get either the eastern or the western volume of Peterson's field guides, or the volume on Texas and adjacent states (*see* Book List). These can be purchased only in hardback editions. If you stay within the area covered by any one of these three volumes, that one is all you will need. But if you travel across Peterson's division lines you will need one of the other Peterson books. The western volume is the only North American field guide that includes the birds of Hawaii. Peterson's guides are highly regarded and are the most widely used of all the North American guides.

3. Other books about birds and bird watching. See the Book List for a good but short list. For still other books, see the "Suggested Reference Material" in *A Guide to Bird Finding*, by Pettingill, and also ask your librarian what books are available on the library shelves. Many bird books, in their book lists (or bibliographies), will refer you to other books.

4. Binoculars. These will "bring the bird nearer to you." For ordinary bird watching in the early stages, high magnification is not necessary. In fact, you cannot see birds less than 30 or 40 feet away, except as a blur, through high-

power glasses. And such glasses are too heavy for ready use, because it is hard to hold them steady and focus them properly at the same time.

If money is no problem, go ahead and buy a good pair of 7 x 35 glasses, and use them from the start. Almost all binoculars now offered for sale have central focusing and coated lenses, but be sure yours do have both.

If money *is* important, here are five suggestions:

(a) Watch birds without using optical equipment until you feel the need for stronger vision.

(b) Ask someone to check the pawnshops for a used pair of old-fashioned opera glasses. These are not in great demand, and often may be bought for very little. They magnify by three or four diameters. This is enough for ordinary day-to-day use.

(c) Look into the possibility of getting binoculars with trading stamps.

(d) Window-shop, and watch the advertisements of camera shops and department stores, for sales on optical equipment. You may be able to get a serviceable pair of Japanese-made binoculars for something between fifteen and twenty-five dollars. Save up your money and when a good bargain comes along, buy yourself a pair.

5. Bird-song phonograph records. These are rather expensive, but very useful. If you can have access to them (perhaps at a library or at the home of a bird watcher who owns them) they will speed up your ability to identify birds by sound. Since you will often hear birds you cannot see, this skill is important. It is even more important because the identification of a bird you *can* see may be doubtful until its song or call settles the problem.

For each of the Peterson field guides there is a record

55

to match—bird by bird, page by page. *A Field Guide to Bird Songs* and *A Field Guide to Western Bird Songs* are both recorded by the Laboratory of Ornithology, Cornell University, and are published by Houghton Mifflin Co. The price is around $12.50 for an album.

If you can find a way to listen to these, do just that. Listen, and listen, and *listen*. Each bird's name is announced, then followed by the song and call (or the scold). Repeated listening will build a connection in your brain between each bird's name and the sound that follows that name.

The Audubon Society's catalog of publications lists a number of other bird-song records.

6. The Audubon Society. Membership in the National Audubon Society also includes membership in your local Audubon Society, if there is one. In addition, it makes you a paid subscriber to the *Audubon Magazine*, issued six times a year.

   The Audubon Society also publishes a quarterly magazine called *Audubon Field Notes*. Each year the April issue (all 400 or more pages of it) is the full report of the Society's Christmas Bird Count—by far the biggest single activity of North American bird watchers.

   Your local Audubon Society may have a nature center, a wildlife refuge, or a bird sanctuary—or all three—where you, as a member, will be welcome. It will probably conduct a series of field trips each year, led by the Society's naturalist or by veteran bird watchers. It may also publish a newsletter, and it may provide a printed checklist for your area, showing what birds you may expect to find where you live and nearby, and when you may expect to find them there.

   The National Audubon Society also informs bird watchers and other lovers of wildlife of present dangers or proposals that threaten birds and other animals, and it speaks and acts for its members in going on from "Live and let live" to "Live and *help* live."

7. The Christmas Bird Count. This is the big climax of the bird watchers' year throughout the United States and Canada. Putting aside holiday festivities, more than 25,000 people voluntarily get up before dawn to go out into the cold, rain, ice, snow, and wintry blasts. They devote all of the particular day set for their area (and on into the night) to the counting of *all the species, and all the individual birds of each species,* found during that one day within circles fifteen miles in diameter.

At the end of 1966, in the fifty states and ten Canadian provinces, 863 groups conducted such counts, each in a separate fifteen-mile circle.

It's strenuous, but it's fun. It's educational, and it's a big contribution to natural science. It has been going on since 1900, and each year it gets bigger. But it is just one of the many activities of the National Audubon Society.

BOOK LIST

For Young People

BLOUGH, GLENN O. *Bird Watchers and Bird Feeders*. Illustrated by Jeanne Bendick. New York: McGraw-Hill Book Co., 1963. How to make feeders; what to feed various birds; which birds to expect when; questions to ask in identifying them; birdbanding; keeping a bird diary.

HANCOCK, DAVNEY. *My Book of Birds*. Baltimore: Ottenheimer Publishers. Big pictures and short introductions to 29 species, several of them not widely familiar.

HISER, IONA SEIBERT. *From Scales to Fancy Feathers*. Illustrated by Anne Marie Jauss. Chicago: Rand McNally & Co., 1962. This book is about the origins of birds, their structure and function, their mating habits; it also tells about, and shows, particular bird groups, and lists 25 bird sanctuaries throughout the United States.

WILLIAMSON, MARGARET. *The First Book of Birds*. New York: Franklin Watts, 1951. How birds came to be, how they are put together, how they behave and why; mating, nest building, brooding, and care for their young; and much else. Some advice about bird watching, attracting birds, etc.

For Beginners of Any Age

PETERSON, ROGER TORY. *How to Know the Birds: An Introduction to Bird Recognition.* (Signet Book). New York: New American Library. (*See* text, page 14, for recommendation.)

ZIM, HERBERT S., AND GABRIELSON, IRA N. *Birds: A Guide to the Most Familiar Birds.* (Golden Nature Guide.) New York: Golden Press, 1949. (*See* text, page 14, for recommendation.)

Field Guides for Everybody

PETERSON, ROGER TORY. *A Field Guide to the Birds.* (Eastern United States and Canada.) Boston: Houghton Mifflin Co.

——*A Field Guide to the Birds of Britain and Europe.* Boston: Houghton Mifflin Co.

——*A Field Guide to the Birds of Texas and Adjacent States.* Boston: Houghton Mifflin Co.

——*A Field Guide to Western Birds.* Boston: Houghton Mifflin Co.

All the books in this series follow the Peterson system, which is based on "patternistic" drawings emphasizing the key field marks as seen at a glance or at a distance, and indicating them with pointer-lines. It also introduces comparisons between similar species; and it first used bird silhouettes for help in sight identification. These books are very good guides indeed. For Texans and their neighbors, the bridge-over Texas book heals the split coverage there of the two earlier books. And for visitors to Europe the "Britain and Europe" volume stands alone in its field. It uses map-charts to show ranges of species. (*See* text, page 54, for recommendation.)

POUGH, RICHARD H. *Audubon Land Bird Guide: Small Land Birds of Eastern and Central North America.* Garden City, N.Y. Doubleday & Co., 1949.

——*Audubon Water Bird Guide: Water, Game, and Large Land Birds of Eastern and Central North America from Southern Texas to Central Greenland.* Garden City, N.Y. Doubleday & Co., 1951.

——*Audubon Western Bird Guide.* Garden City, N.Y.: Doubleday & Co., 1957.

Pough's guides include more detail about nests, eggs, and habits than do other popular guides, but they lack comparisons with similar species. Many bird watchers like to use Pough's guides at home to find out more about the birds seen or to help pinpoint a problem bird, but they find that Peterson's compact eastern or western guides or the single-volume Robbins-Bruun-Zim guide give quicker access to important identifying details in the field. Pough's illustrations are grouped together in the middle of the book, and are somewhat crowded.

ROBBINS, CHANDLER S., BRUUN, BERTEL, AND ZIM, HERBERT S. *Birds of North America: A Guide to Field Identification.* Illustrated by Arthur Singer. (Golden Field Guide.) New York: Golden Press, 1966. Hardback and paperback. This guide is the only one that fully covers in one compact volume all species of all North America north of Mexico (and insofar as we share species with Mexico, of Mexico as well). The paperback edition, besides being far less expensive than any other book of comparable coverage, is lightweight and not too thick for pocket use in the field. All pictures are in full color, and all illustrations are directly facing the descriptions they illustrate. Color-keyed diagrams on maps show at a glance not only the range of a species, but also its breeding, migrating, and wintering areas. This guide's "sonagram" pictures of bird songs are hard to translate from the eye to the ear, however.

For Library Exploration

ALLEN, ARTHUR A. *The Book of Bird Life.* Photographs by the author; paintings by Dr. W. C. Dilger. Princeton, N. J.: D. Van Nostrand Co., 1961. Very readable, but not simplified. In two main parts: (1) The Living Bird. About the birds themselves—their history, classification, distribution, migration, habitats, courtship, home life, adaptation, plumage, and relation to mankind. (2) Methods of Bird Study. About bird walks, record-keeping, birdbanding, attracting birds, nests, observation blinds, photography, bird songs, birds as pets, suggestions for specialized study, and suggested books for bird watching.

This book is used as an ornithology textbook at Dr. Allen's longtime base of operations, Cornell University, but a really interested student in intermediate or junior high school could follow most of it fairly well.

——*Stalking Birds with Color Camera.* Washington, D. C.: National Geographic Society, 1963. Includes 494 illustrations; 385 are natural-color photographs. Dr. Allen had an unquenchable interest in birds and in photography, and he was persistent in his pursuit of these interests. Like Forbush, he made birds come alive when he wrote about them. In this book he did it with words and pictures together.

FORBUSH, EDWARD HOWE. *A Natural History of American Birds of Eastern and Central North America.* Revised and abridged, with the addition of over 100 species by John Richard May. Illustrated by Louis Agassiz Fuertes, Allan Brooks, and Roger Tory Peterson. (Bramhall Books.) New York: Clarkson

N. Potter. Because so many eastern species are seen also in the west, every North American bird watcher can learn much from this big book and find much to enjoy. Descriptions of and comments about many species are much more detailed than those in any field guide. Mr. Forbush was a master story teller as well as a great authority on birds. To learn more about the birds you already know, try this book.

HVASS, HANS. *Birds of the World in Color.* Translated by Gwynne Vevers. New York: E. P. Dutton & Co., 1964. Presents 1,100 species, many of them to be found in North America or Europe. There is a short introduction to each family of birds. Individual species are described in 15 to 50 words, with a color illustration. Not a field guide, but a reference book good to know.

LIFE. *The Birds,* by Roger Tory Peterson and the editors of *Life.* (*Life* Nature Library.) New York: Time, Inc. How so much could be fitted into a 92-page book is hard to understand. If your library does not have this book, inquire among your friends in the hope of borrowing it. (You might find it in a secondhand bookstore.) Excellent background information, magnificent photographs. Strongly recommended.

LINCOLN, FREDERICK C. *Migration of Birds.* Illustrated by Bob Hines. (Circular 16, Fish and Wildlife Services, U. S. Dept. of the Interior.) For sale by the Superintendent of Documents, U.S. Government Printing Office, Washington, D. C. Price, 35 cents. An understanding of migration is important to bird watchers. In addition to its text, this circular of 102 pages lists 102 references to books or magazine articles on the subject, stating "only a few can be listed in this publication."

PETTINGILL, OLIN SEWALL, JR. *A Guide to Bird Finding East of the Mississippi.* New York: Oxford University Press, 1951.
——*A Guide to Bird Finding West of the Mississippi.* New York: Oxford University Press, 1953.

Besides describing exactly where you should go and how to get there, and what birds you can expect to find there and when—in all the continental United States and Canada—this book contains a full list of books and other reference material, with particular emphasis on field guides and other publications on the birds of regions, individual states, and parts of states. It also lists books on national parks and monuments and on wildlife refuges. A practical, factual pair of reference books for the bird watcher who can travel about the country.

WETMORE, ALEXANDER, AND OTHERS. *Song and Garden Birds of North America*. Washington, D. C.: National Geographic Society, 1964. (Includes a small album of bird-song recordings.) Shows 327 species in color and describes them; 555 illustrations altogether.

——*Water, Prey, and Game Birds of North America*. Washington, D. C.: National Geographic Society, 1965. A companion volume to *Song and Garden Birds of North America*. (Includes a small album of bird-song recordings.) Shows and describes 329 species; 600 color illustrations.

In both these volumes, each of several experts tells about the bird groups he knows best. The experts wrote not to be read in a hurry, but to tell the whole story. From these books you will learn much that is new to you.

INDEX

65